x find your way

UNDER THE SEA

Paul Boston

YOUR MISSION

Welcome to Merp Town. We need your help to finish building our castle. Find your way there by choosing which exits or entrances to follow on each page.

1

Choose your transport

Submarine

Sea Turtle

Seahorse

2

Trace a route

There are lots to choose from and you can go **BACKWARDS** and **FORWARDS** along the same road.

3

Collect on every page

Choose ONE of the missions below to help the Merps. You will find one of each object in every scene.

Collect **12 SHINY PEARLS** to decorate the princess's bedroom.

Collect **12 BURGERS** for the hungry castle builders.

Collect **12 SHARK TEETH** to use as tools to help build the castle.

4

Use the book LIKE A REAL MAP

Turn the pages and use co-ordinates in this book just like you would with a real map. You can find out more about co-ordinates on pages 4 and 5.

5

Solve maths puzzles

Along the way you will come across Merps who are lost or need your help. You will have to use your super maths skills to help them. You might be asked to count up to ten or to find a shape.

Welcome to Merp Town

Look at the map of Merp Town. Can you see where the castle is? That's where you need to get to. Let's use co-ordinates to help us describe where the castle is on the map.

A

Octopus Junction
Pages 6-7

START HERE

3

B

Kelp Forest
Pages 8-9

Hot Water Springs
Pages 14-15

2

Glow Squid Cave
Pages 16-17

Shipwreck Site
Pages 22-23

1

Jellyfish Jungle
Pages 24-25

When reading co-ordinates:
Go ACROSS the seabed first, and then UP the seaweed.

A

B

4

What are co-ordinates?

Co-ordinates are a set of letters and numbers that show where something is on a map. The letter comes first, followed by the number, so the castle is in **(D,1)**. Look for the co-ordinate symbol throughout the book.

C

Skeleton Cove
Pages 10–11

Old Town
Pages 12–13

D

3

Sinkhole Hollow
Pages 18–19

Snoozy Sea Dragon
Pages 20–21

2

Anemone Villas
Pages 26–27

The Royal Quarter
Pages 28–29

FINISH

C

D

Oh no! Mr Tentacles is blocking the way! Find a way around him to carry on with your mission. Use your finger to help. Can you spot your object anywhere?

SHARK TOOTH

BURGER

PEARL

◎ I'm lost! Can you please tell me the co-ordinates for the bank?

START HERE

Stop! Count how many shoes Mr Tentacles is missing before I let you pass.

OCTOPUS JUNCTION

AQUA PETS

Go to page 14

HOT WATER SPRINGS

A

C

3

2

1

A

C

6

Go to page 9
KELP FOREST

Go to page 9
KELP FOREST

Go to page 18
SINKHOLE HOLLOW

Go to page 23
JELLYFISH JUNGLE

MORE FUN UNDER THE SEA!

Understanding Co-ordinates

Encourage your child to look at other places where they might find co-ordinates, such as on an A-Z map. Draw a pirate's map together and plan your route to the treasure, or play a game of Battleships.

Counting

Go back through the book and look for more opportunities to encourage counting under the sea. How many arms does an octopus have? How many claws does a crab have?

Telling the Time

Make a simple clock with your child to encourage them to look closely at telling the time. Use a paper plate, and attach arms using a split pin or pipe cleaners. You could even decorate it to look like a turtle. Fill in the clock face using coloured pens. To go a step further, make paper 'flaps' which can be lifted up to reveal the minutes.

Recognising Shapes

Make a sea monster! Cut out lots of different 2D shapes from coloured paper. You could use triangles for the flippers, a circle for the body and squares for its scales. What shape would its teeth be? You could even try using 3D shapes from plasticine.

Maths Problems and Vocabulary

Go back through the book and look for opportunities to build on mathematic vocabulary and problem solving skills. For example, what is the total number of baby squid? Or, if there are three jellyfish with ten legs each, how many legs are there altogether?

Measurements

Using building blocks, make a little underwater town with your child. Can you make a really tall block of flats like the Anemone Villas? What about a long boat or a short submarine?

Quarto Knows

Quarto is the authority on a wide range of topics.
Quarto educates, entertains and enriches the lives of our readers—enthusiasts and lovers of hands-on living.
www.quartoknows.com

Written and edited by: Joanna McInerney and the QED team
Designer: Mike Henson
Consultant: Alistair Bryce-Clegg

2016 © Quarto Publishing plc

This edition first published in paperback in 2018 by QED Publishing, an imprint of The Quarto Group.

The Old Brewery, 6 Blundell Street,
London N7 9BH, United Kingdom.
T (0)20 7700 6700 F (0)20 7700 8066
www.QuartoKnows.com

A catalogue record for this book is available from the British Library.

ISBN 978 1 78493 286 2

Manufactured in Guangdong, China TT042018

9 8 7 6 5 4 3 2 1